DOODLING
Dinosaurs

Words by
Simon Tudhope

Designed by
Krysia Ellis
Candice Whatmore
Jenny Brown

Let's get going!

2

I've got the
LONGEST NECK.

I'm the
SPIKIEST!

There are too many dinosaurs in this bath!

5

6

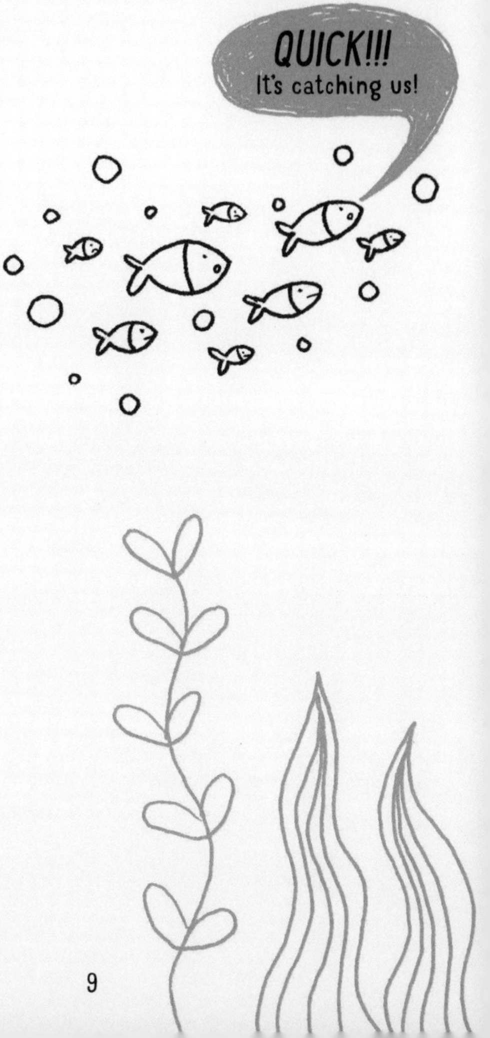
QUICK!!!
It's catching us!

11

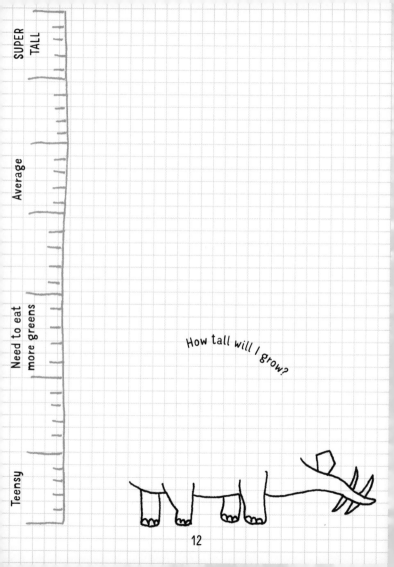

SUPER TALL

Average

Need to eat more greens

Teensy

How tall will I grow?

12

How about me?

And me?

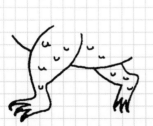

14

DRIED
LEAVES

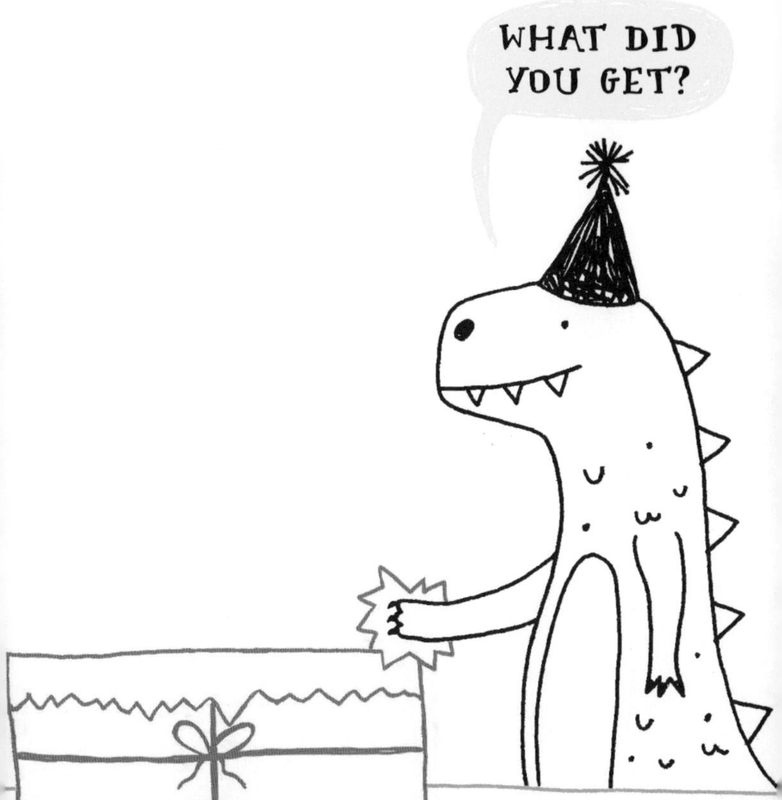
WHAT DID YOU GET?

Family day out

20

Funny faces

First day at school

21

23

WORLD'S **UGLIEST** DINOSAUR

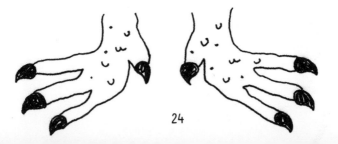

25

26

27

HMMM...
What's for lunch?

29

30

31